Corncrakes

naturally scottish

Corncrakes

naturally scottish

by

Rhys Green & Helen Riley

SCOTTISH
NATURAL
HERITAGE

SNH Publications, Battleby, Redgorton, Perth, Scotland

First published in 1999
This edition publishedin 2005
by Scottish Natural Heritage,
Battleby, Redgorton, Perth, PH1 3EW
Tel: 01738 458530 Fax: 01738 458613
E-mail: pubs@snh.gov.uk
Web site: www.snh.org.uk

Designed and produced by SNH Publications

Photographs: Niall Benvie 13, 23, 24 **Laurie Campbell** vi, 6, 8, 25 **Frances Furlong/Survival Anglia**
19 bottom left **Simon Kench/RSPCA** 14 **Keith Ringland** 2, 3 **RSPB** 10 left
Norbert Schäfer v, 7 bottom, 9, 10 right, 16, 22 **C.Self** 1, 12, 21 left, 21 right **B.S.Turner/FLPA** viii
G.Tyler 19 bottom right **David Whitaker vii, 20 Alan Williams/NHPA** cover, i, back cover
Illustrations: John Tasker

ISBN 1 85397 049 2 paperback
A CIP record is held at the British Library.
W2K0305

Contents

Foreword

Shanks are honoured to have been recognised by the Government as Champion for the Corncrake Biodiversity Action Plan. We want to play our part in helping those who are involved in this plan, in particular The Scottish Executive, The Royal Society for the Protection of Birds (RSPB) and Scottish Natural Heritage (SNH), to support the corncrake.

Our interest in biodiversity is part of our commitment to sustainable development and we recognise the responsibilities that are placed on us to preserve our natural heritage for generations to come. This publication will help to raise the awareness of a wider public about the corncrake and the efforts that are being made to conserve it as part of our natural heritage. Shanks are delighted to support it.

Angus Maclauchlan
Marketing Manager, Shanks

shanks. waste solutions.

Shanks is the largest waste management company in the UK with a heritage that goes back over 100 years. Shanks offers waste solutions tailored to meet individual company needs, working in partnership with customers, local authorities and regulatory bodies.

SCOTTISH
BIODIVERSITY
GROUP

Introduction

Many people who live in the midst of corncrakes have never seen one, but know them only by their distinctive song. Corncrakes are secretive, skulking birds with strong legs and feet ideal for propelling them through the tall grass and rough vegetation where they spend nearly all of their time. Although they would once have been familiar to all country dwellers in Britain, a decline over the past 150 years has meant that corncrakes are now confined to the northern and western fringes of Scotland.

1

Corncrake meadows, Coll

What is a corncrake?

Corncrakes are related to moorhens, coots and rails, a family of 133 species of birds with a world-wide distribution. Corncrakes are similar in shape to moorhens but slightly smaller in size. Males and females are virtually indistinguishable - both having plumage streaked with a subtle combination of brown and grey except for the beautiful bright chestnut wings which show up in flight. Corncrakes differ from most other members of the rail family because they live on dry land, and are not adapted to wade or swim in marshes and ponds. Birds that visit Scotland in the summer to breed, migrate to Africa for the winter months.

Why call it a corncrake?

The name corncrake (originally 'corne crake' or 'cornecraik') dates from the 15th century and originated in Scotland. It was adopted in England at the end of the 18th Century and largely superseded the alternative name of 'land-rail'. In Gaelic the most commonly used name is traon, which refers to the call, but there are many other descriptive Gaelic names for corncrake as listed in the box below along with their English translations.

The "crake" in corncrake refers to its voice, but the "corn" is harder to justify. Today corncrakes are most often found in fields of grass grown for hay or silage. They sometimes use oats and barley in Scotland in late summer, after hay has been mowed, and they probably used cereal fields more often in the past, before pesticides and herbicides were used and when there were more insects and other small animals for them to eat. In eastern Europe, where fewer pesticides are used, corncrakes occur much more often in cornfields than in western Europe, but, even there, grassland is the main habitat.

GAELIC NAMES FOR THE CORNCRAKE

Traon	most commonly used, refers to the call
Bramach-roid	'fast running rasper'
Cleabhair-caoch	'nutty noisemaker'
Corra-ghoirtean	'long-legged bird of the little cornfield'
Dreòghann	perhaps related to the Gaelic name for wren (dreathann)
Garra-gart	'bird of the standing corn/cornfield'
Rac-an-arbhair	'croaker of the corn'
Rac an fheòir	'croaker of the grass'
Trèan-ri-trèan	refers to the call

The corncrake's song

The corncrake has a loud, rasping call. Where corncrakes are present, this distinctive call can be heard by day or night any time between April and August, but the best chance of hearing the corncrake's song is between 11 pm and 3 am in June and early July.

To the human ear the corncrake's song is a repetitive 'crek, crek' with the tempo of a ringing telephone. Analysis by a sonograph shows that each rendition of the song lasts less than a second and consists of two strings of about fifteen short but powerful pulses of sound, one hundredth of a second apart, generated in the bird's chest and broadcast through the loud-hailer of its open mouth. The human ear cannot resolve the pulses, so we just hear two rather harsh notes. However, people in many different countries have learned to imitate corncrakes by scraping a hard edge against a notched wooden wheel or notched cow rib bone - which

produces a similar chain of sound pulses. The modern equivalent is a comb and plastic credit card.

Un-musical as it may seem, the song of the male corncrake is used to attract females. In fact it is usually only male corncrakes that sing, though females are capable of producing a quiet version on rare occasions. During the spring and early summer, males sing almost continuously for four hours every night. This means that in the course of a summer a typical male corncrake repeats himself between half a million and a million times! Unless something disturbs him, a male corncrake usually sings from the same place every night until he attracts a mate. Once he has a female the male will stay close to her for the next few days while the pair mate and the female begins to lay a clutch of eggs. During this period the male sings much less frequently.

This graph of air pressure changes shows that the crek-crek song of the corncrake consists of two short bursts of spiky pulses. This male has 16 pulses in the first crek and 19 in the second.

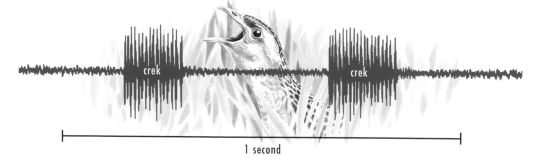

crek   crek

1 second

Migration

Corncrakes breed in Europe and western Siberia and migrate every winter to the grasslands and savannahs of central and southern Africa, crossing the deserts of the Middle East and North Africa on the way. Birds that breed in Scotland leave here in September and October and return in April and May. They usually travel at night and probably fly at a fairly low height, judging by the fact that they sometimes collide with overhead power cables and lighthouses. Exactly what route the birds from Scotland follow is unknown. Only one corncrake ringed in Scotland has been recovered from the wintering grounds and this was from the Congo in central Africa.

Corncrakes are rarely seen in flight and then usually only when they are disturbed. In flight they trail their legs, stay close to the ground and usually dive back into the cover of tall vegetation as soon as possible. This has led people to assume that they are poor fliers, but this is a misconception. Corncrakes are not fast and manoeuvrable in flight and could not outpace a hunting bird of prey, so they are safest when in cover. However, they undertake some of the longest migrations known amongst birds -sometimes getting lost and turning up in places as far flung as Vietnam, New Zealand and North America. So, whilst their navigation system might not always work perfectly, corncrakes have the endurance to travel great distances.

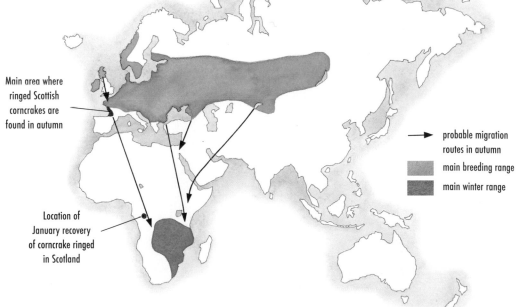

World distribution of corncrakes

Main area where ringed Scottish corncrakes are found in autumn

Location of January recovery of corncrake ringed in Scotland

→ probable migration routes in autumn

main breeding range

main winter range

One of the remaining strongholds of the corncrake in Scotland is the *machair* of South Uist where low-intensity hay and silage production and arable cropping are continued by crofters.

Habitat

Except on the long migratory flight, corncrakes spend nearly all of their lives concealed in tall grass or herbaceous vegetation, such as nettles or cow parsley. Before humans changed the landscape, much of Britain was covered by forests. Corncrakes were probably then confined to grassland habitats such as riverside meadows or coastal grasslands; areas where trees could not grow because of grazing by deer and wild cattle or through flooding or wild fires. Today most corncrakes live on farmed grassland where mowing and grazing by livestock produce the right kind of vegetation.

Corncrakes require plant cover that is at least 20 cm tall (a hand's span) so that it hides them completely. Such habitat can be in short supply in the spring in Scotland when corncrakes begin to arrive back from migration. In April, the combination of grazing and winter weather often leaves only a few patches of tall vegetation in the form of nettles or yellow flag iris and these will form important 'early cover' refuges for corncrakes.

Where hay and silage is grown, there will be fields of grass which are tall enough for corncrakes to use by early summer. Then they will no longer be confined to the small areas of early cover, but have larger fields to

By fencing both sides of a ditch between two silage fields to exclude mowing and grazing a corridor of reed and cow parsley has been created to provide early cover for corncrakes.

wander through. Once hay and silage crops have been cut later in the summer, corncrakes are again confined to smaller areas that remain un-mowed and un-grazed, so the patches of yellow flag and nettles often become their refuge again.

When they are singing at night, males prefer to be amongst robust or woody stems, such as willow bushes or dead reeds and cow parsley from the previous year's growth. Perhaps this makes them safer from prowling cats and other predators during their night-time singing, because they then seem oblivious to rustling caused by nearby movements - perhaps unable to hear anything above their own voices!

Not all vegetation that is tall enough for corncrakes is actually suitable. Stands of dead grass from the previous year's growth and beds of rushes are often so dense that the birds find it difficult to creep through them and they cannot see the ground surface to look for food. Tall, closely spaced grasses in fertilised meadows may be equally dense, and they are certainly so when pushed to the ground, or 'lodged', by wind and rain. Corncrakes prefer grasslands where much of the annual growth of leaves is removed between late summer and winter by mowing, grazing or winter floods, and the grass is allowed to grow back in the spring to a sufficient height to provide good cover. On fertile soils, the vegetation in abandoned meadows tends to become too dense for corncrakes within a year or two.

Food

In the breeding season corncrakes eat a wide range of small animals pecked from plants or from the soil surface and plant litter. Earthworms, beetles, slugs and snails are the main prey in Scotland. Females feed young chicks on a similar diet until they learn to forage for themselves.

Breeding

A female corncrake may well pick out her mate's song from the air at the end of her long spring migration flight. The male sings much less often once paired and the pair stay close together for a few days. During this time the female inspects nest sites already prepared by the male

The blurring on this photograph reveals the rapid movement of the singing male corncrake's beak.

and chooses one of them. Early in the season, most nests are concealed in stands of nettles, cow parsley or yellow flag, usually within 200 metres of the male's singing place. Once a nest is selected, the female begins to lay eggs at the rate of one and sometimes two per day. The eggs are about half the size of hens' eggs and have red-brown spots on a greenish-grey background. The pair separates before half of the 8-12 egg clutch is laid. The male then resumes his nocturnal singing - usually from a different position and sometimes a considerable distance away. With luck he will attract another female. Most females lay a second clutch later in the summer and they may also move before doing so. Hence both males and females are likely to change partners between breeding attempts.

Corncrakes nest on the ground. The nest is about the size of a saucer, hidden away in dense vegetation and constructed from dead stems and leaves collected nearby. The female incubates the eggs alone for the 17-18 days before they hatch. During this time she leaves the nest for 10-15 minutes every hour and searches for food within a few metres of the nest before returning to warm the eggs. When they hatch, the chicks are covered in jet-black down. They leave the nest for good soon after

9   *Young corncrake chicks depend on their mother for food and compete for her attention. A greater proportion of chicks from large broods die during their first two weeks because of this competition.*

hatching, but are fed and brooded [kept warm] by the female as they gradually begin to catch prey for themselves.

At night the female builds a temporary nest in which the chicks roost. They develop rapidly and brown feathers soon begin to sprout through the down, but they still look vulnerable when abandoned by their mother to fend for themselves at about 12 days old. From this time onwards the chicks will live independently but they are unable to fly until they are about 35 days old. Remarkably, they begin their migration and leave the breeding area as soon as the growth of their flight feathers is complete - at about 45 days old.

After leaving her first family, the female immediately joins a singing male and lays a second clutch of eggs. By this time it is late June or early July. These second nests are usually established in hay and silage meadows where the grass has now grown tall enough for corncrakes to use. The female cares for her second family in a similar way to the first, but stays with the chicks for rather longer - 15-20 days - because there is by then no rush to lay yet more eggs. By the time the second brood of young leave the nest it is late July or even August, but ringing studies have shown that these late-hatched young have as good a chance of surviving to the following year as the chicks from first broods, hatched earlier in the season.

A nest in which a female corncrake has recently laid the first of ten eggs is well hidden in grass and nettles.

Corncrake mother and chick

Corncrake displays

A male singing to attract a female
or deter an intruding rival male ▷

◁ A male displays its striking
chestnut wings to a rival

This threat posture is used before a fight
breaks out between rival males ▷

◁ A male courting a potential mate shows
off his chestnut wings to the full

Illustrations from The Birds of the Western Palearctic, Volume II. Handbook of the Birds of Europe
and the Middle East and North Africa, eds S Cramp and KEL Simmons, 1980. Reproduced by
permission of Oxford University Press.

Lifespan

In areas where they are still numerous, there has often been a corncrake singing in spring from exactly the same patch of yellow flag for years. It is easy to imagine that this is the same bird returning again and again, but it turns out that this is usually not the case. Only about one in five of the adult corncrakes present each spring will survive to the next. The rest perish. This means that the majority of the males singing in a given spring were actually born in the previous year. Most young males return to within a few kilometres of their birthplace; some to the very patch of iris or nettles from which they hatched. So the corncrake that has "returned" to rasp out his song in the same spot as last year is more likely to be the son of his predecessor.

Female corncrakes are thought to be less faithful to their origins than males, but because they do not sing and are harder to study, much less is known about their movements.

Because most corncrakes will only survive for one year, every breeding corncrake must produce large numbers of young each year to maintain the overall numbers. It has been estimated that each breeding female must rear 5 chicks each year to keep the population in a given area stable. Corncrake populations can decline very rapidly if they are unable to breed successfully and produce enough fledged chicks to replace the adult birds that die.

Everything that is known about the lifespan and movements of corncrakes comes from recoveries and recaptures of adults and chicks caught and individually marked with numbered metal leg rings.

Because they are difficult to see, much of our detailed knowledge of corncrakes comes from tracking the movements of radio-tagged birds.

Causes of death

The machinery used to cut fields of hay and silage poses a major threat to the survival of corncrakes on their breeding grounds and has been linked to the decline of this species. This is explained in more detail later on.

Domestic cats can be significant predators of corncrakes. Fitting a collar with a bell may help the birds to hear the cat coming.

Other threats to corncrakes in the breeding season are predation by domestic and feral cats, mink, otters and birds of prey. Less frequently, corncrakes may die after colliding with wire fences, overhead wires and road traffic.

Although there are many reports of adult corncrakes taken by predators there are no clear links between predator abundance, the death rate of adult corncrakes and population trends. Indeed the spectacular population declines of corncrakes in Britain in the late 19th and early 20th centuries began when the killing of birds of prey, crows and predatory mammals by gamekeepers was at its height. A recent study found that the death rate of adult corncrakes during the breeding season was higher in an increasing population than in a declining population. Presumably greater losses of adults were offset by more successful breeding in the increasing population. One obvious difference between the two populations studied was the amount of cover available to the birds in spring and early summer. The population with the lower death rate had more early cover.

Some cats learn to stalk singing males and the relatively tall vegetation in gardens and around farm buildings in spring can bring corncrakes and cats perilously close together. Predators seem to catch corncrakes most often when they are located in small patches of tall vegetation which are easy for the predator to search, or where corncrakes are conspicuous when forced to move across open ground between patches of cover. For this reason, increasing the area and continuity of suitable tall cover at times of year when it is scarce is likely to reduce the death rate of adults.

Corncrake nests are remarkably immune from predators. Even in areas where the eggs of other birds are being taken by crows, rats, hedgehogs and other predators, it is unusual for a predator to find and take the eggs from a corncrake nest. The extremely careful concealment of the nest in tall vegetation and the secretive behaviour of the incubating female probably pay off in making it very difficult to detect.

Predators also take less of a toll of corncrake chicks than is the case for many other species with small flightless young. About half of the young that hatch survive to become independent. However, this proportion can be much lower if chicks get caught up in the mowing of hay and silage.

Very little is known about the hazards faced by corncrakes away from the breeding grounds because they are such elusive birds. In winter when they do not sing, it is difficult to know where they are. Some

Corncrakes from eastern Europe are shot and trapped whilst on autumn migration on the Mediterranean coast of Egypt. These nets are set to catch quail, but they also catch corncrakes.

corncrakes are shot on autumn migration by hunters in southern Europe. Many are trapped and shot along the Mediterranean coast of Egypt. However, the numbers involved, though quite large, represent only a tiny proportion of the corncrake population which migrates through Egypt from eastern Europe where the species is still widespread. Corncrakes ringed in Scotland have never been reported from Egypt. Their direct route to the wintering grounds from western France, where they pause in September, is likely to take them further west in North Africa, where trapping and shooting are not known to occur on so large a scale (see map on page 5).

On the wintering grounds in Africa no definite threats to corncrakes have been established. Locally, burning of grasslands or overgrazing may displace birds, but some experts think that the felling of woodland has increased the area of potentially suitable habitat.

The vanishing corncrake

Writing about the break-up of fields close to Edinburgh for building in the first half of the nineteenth century, the Advocate Lord Cockburn laments the beginning of a sad change. In 'Memorials of his Time', he describes that "I have stood in Queen Street, or the opening at the north-west corner of Charlotte Square, and listened to the ceaseless rural corn-craiks, nestling happily in the dewy grass." At this time, corncrakes bred in every county of Britain. No-one attempted to count them, but there must have been tens of thousands.

Declines in corncrake populations were noticed as long ago as the latter half of the 19th century in Britain and several other European countries. By 1940 corncrakes in Britain were only found in large numbers in the Hebrides and the Northern Isles of Scotland, though many parts of

16

mainland Scotland and northern England held smaller populations.

The decline in corncrake numbers in Britain in the late 19th and early 20th centuries began at different times in different areas. In each case, the beginning of the decline coincided with the introduction of horse-drawn mowing machines which were able to cut larger areas of grass in one session than was previously possible by hand.

Mechanised mowing is dangerous to corncrakes because they live in hay and silage fields and are reluctant to move out of tall vegetation. Virtually all corncrake nests in meadows are destroyed when they are mowed. Adults - including incubating females - and chicks run away from the mower into uncut grass. If the mower is operating from the edges of the field inwards - which is usually the case - it herds all the corncrakes in the field into the ever-decreasing area of uncut grass in the centre. Adults and fledged young can fly out of the remaining area of grass when it becomes so small they can no longer escape the mower, but flightless chicks are often killed as the mower cuts the last few swaths in the centre of the field. Mowing from the outside of a field inwards kills up to 60% of any corncrake chicks present. Chicks which do attempt to escape, by crossing the open area of the field that has been mowed, may be snapped up by predators such as gulls.

19th century

1990s

There has been a huge reduction in the breeding range (shading) of the corncrake in Britain in the last 100 years.

ROAST LANDRAIL, OR CORN-CRAKE.

1033. INGREDIENTS.—3 or 4 birds, butter, fried bread crumbs.

LANDRAILS.

Mode.—Pluck and draw the birds, wipe them inside and out with damp cloths, and truss them in the following manner :—Bring the head round under the wing, and the thighs close to the sides ; pass a skewer through them and the body, and keep the legs straight. Roast them before a clear fire, keep them well basted, and serve on fried bread crumbs, with a tureen of brown gravy. When liked, bread-sauce may also be sent to table with them.

Time.—12 to 20 minutes. *Average cost.*—Seldom bought.

Sufficient.—Allow 4 for a dish.

Seasonable from August 12th to the middle of September.

THE LANDRAIL, OR CORN-CRAKE.—This bird is migratory in its habits, yet from its formation, it seems ill adapted for long aërial passages, its wings being short, and placed so forward out of the centre of gravity, that it flies in an extremely heavy and embarrassed manner, and with its legs hanging down. When it alights, it can hardly be sprung a second time, as it runs very fast, and seems to depend for its safety more on the swiftness of its feet than the celerity of its wings. It makes its appearance in England about the same time as the quail, that is, in the months of April and May, and frequents the same places. Its singular cry is first heard when the grass becomes long enough to shelter it, and it continues to be heard until the grass is cut. The bird, however, is seldom seen, for it constantly skulks among the thickest portions of the herbage, and runs so nimbly through it, doubling and winding in every direction, that it is difficult to get near it. It leaves this island before the winter, and repairs to other countries in search of its food, which principally consists of slugs, large numbers of which it destroys. It is very common in Ireland, and, whilst migrating to this country, is seen in great numbers in the island of Anglesea. On its first arrival in England, it is so lean as scarcely to weigh above five or six ounces; before its departure, however, it has been known to exceed eight ounces, and is then most delicious eating.

THE LANDRAIL.

In the 19th century, when corncrakes were more widespread, they merited an entry in a famous English cookery book, The Book of Household Management (1861) by Mrs Beeton. Corncrakes caught in September were considered to make the best eating because they were then at their fattest just before the autumn migration to Africa.

Because it is quicker, mechanised mowing also allows the whole hay or silage harvest to be completed earlier in the summer. Hence, with the introduction of horse-drawn mowers, fields which would have been mowed in late summer if mowing was done by hand were harvested earlier, within the breeding period of the corncrake, so a greater proportion of nests and broods were destroyed.

Later in the 20th century, horses were replaced by tractors, resulting in even greater reductions in the time required to harvest the hay crop. Intensification of farming increased, including the development of early maturing grass types, silage technology and fertiliser regimes which allowed harvests to be made earlier and sometimes, for several grass crops to be taken from fields in a given summer. In addition, land drainage allowed people to mow meadows in river floodplains earlier than before. Corncrakes continued to decline and eventually there were so few left that birdwatchers were able to count them. After a rough estimate of 2,500 singing males in 1970, the first full census of Britain in 1978 found about 750, which fell to 570 in 1988 and 480 in 1993. During this period corncrakes almost vanished from England and Wales and only a handful remained on the Scottish mainland.

Corncrakes have survived in the northern and western islands of Scotland. Here, the climate and poor soils, combined with the cultural and social history and the distance to markets, has meant that the agricultural development which caused the population declines elsewhere has not proceeded as quickly or as far. On the Hebrides, grass is still harvested much later than on the mainland, in spite of mechanisation. However, the corncrake populations are still not safe. Mowing has become faster and earlier and the area of suitable tall vegetation for corncrakes has been reduced as land formerly used to grow hay and silage is put to other uses, such as sheep-grazing, or is abandoned altogether as declines in farming affect these areas.

Although mechanisation and intensification of hay and silage making has had adverse effects on corncrakes, this is not to say that farming is bad for corncrakes. In most of

Mowing silage from the outside of the field inwards makes it impossible for corncrakes to escape without a risky run across open ground. Gulls await the chance of a meal.

their world range, and certainly in Scotland, corncrakes depend upon habitats created and maintained by farming and have done so for many years. Abandonment of farming poses a threat to corncrake populations in many areas. The challenge is to find ways in which corncrakes can continue to live on modern farms and crofts.

Corncrake adults and chicks are killed by the mower if they are unable to escape to unmowed habitat

A corncrake nest with eggs smashed during mowing

Corncrake Conservation

There is now a programme of conservation action which aims to reverse the decline of corncrakes in Great Britain. Work is co-ordinated through the Biodiversity Action Plan for corncrakes. The lead partners in this group are the Scottish Executive Rural Affairs Department (SERAD) and the Royal Society for the Protection of Birds (RSPB), supported by a number of other organisations including Scottish Natural Heritage (SNH) and the Scottish Crofters Union (SCU).

The most widely applied actions to date are schemes which provide payments to farmers in corncrake areas to delay mowing hay and silage fields until 1 August or later and to change the method of mowing to reduce the mortality of chicks. Mowing from the centre of the meadow outwards, or using some other 'corncrake-friendly' mowing pattern that allows chicks to escape without leaving the shelter of uncut grass, has been shown to greatly reduce chick deaths. More recently, existing schemes have been expanded or new schemes have been introduced to provide payments for farmers to establish areas of tall native vegetation to act as 'early cover' for corncrakes in the spring and late summer when the grass in meadows is too short for them.

Where land is suitable, management for corncrakes has also become a very high priority on nature reserves and other areas managed for conservation throughout the Scottish islands.

The dumping of manure in field margins during winter encourages vegetation growth to provide cover for corncrakes

Corncrake populations seem to be responding to these measures both locally and nationally. After a century of decline, the corncrake population of Great Britain has begun to increase since conservation measures began in earnest in 1992. In 2004 there were over 1,060 singing males in Britain, more than twice the number recorded in the national survey in 1993.

Corncrakes and the law

Corncrakes are specially protected under the Wildlife and Countryside Act 1981 and it is an offence to shoot or otherwise deliberately kill them or to knowingly to disturb them at the nest or with young. It can also be an offence to be in possession of a corncrake, whether dead or alive, including stuffed birds, without appropriate authority.

Corncrake-friendly mowing

Corncrakes escaping into corridor of tall vegetation that will not be mowed.

Mowing towards rocky knoll to leave a sizeable refuge area of unmown grass.

Corncrake corner and corridor protected from grazing and mowing to provide cover early and late in the season.

After opening up 2 ends the field is mowed from the middle outwards to push corncrakes to the edges.

A bed of yellow flag iris provides cover for corncrakes in spring and after mowing of the adjacent silage field. The fence protects it from grazing livestock. Mowing the silage in a corncrake friendly way (see opposite) would allow flightless corncrake chicks to escape into the iris bed without leaving the cover of tall vegetation.

How can I see corncrakes?

Corncrakes tend to frustrate birdwatchers because they often remain unseen, even though it is obvious from the song where they are. This is why counts of corncrakes are made in terms of the number of calling males heard, rather than the number of birds seen. If you hear a corncrake, you should not disturb the bird or its habitat in the hope of an unsatisfactory glimpse of it running or flying away, but look for a place where a singing bird is likely to have to cross open ground to move from one patch of cover to another. Watching in the early morning or late evening in late May, when daytime singing is frequent and cover tends to be sparse, is most likely to be profitable. Alternatively, like many others, you may simply be content with being able to hear one of our rarest, but most cryptic, birds.

The future

Corncrakes are not just vulnerable in Britain, they are considered to be "near threatened" globally because they are declining in much of their world range. Conservation actions in the UK seem to have halted the long-term decline in corncrakes here and brought about a modest recovery. However the UK population is still small and corncrakes are not out of danger. The steering group for the corncrake action plan will continue to work towards promoting an increase in the numbers and range of corncrakes in Scotland and the re-establishment of this charismatic bird in some of its former haunts elsewhere in the UK. Lessons learned from corncrake conservation actions in Scotland and the rest of the UK may, in time, be applied world-wide to ensure that the call of the corncrake is never silenced.

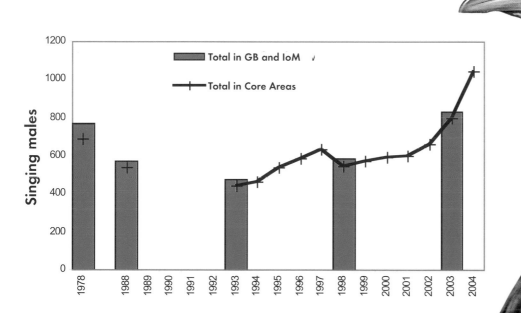

Further reading

Listed below are some useful starting points for anyone who wishes to find out more about corncrakes. There are few publications dealing specifically with these birds so many of the references are for recently published bird handbooks with up to date accounts of corncrakes. Some of these are not readily available and you may have to search for them in specialist libraries.

Biodiversity: the UK Steering Group Report. Volume 2: Action Plans. Published by HMSO, 1995.

Birds in Europe: Their Conservation Status. Edited by G Tucker, M.F. Heath, L. Tomialojc and R.F.A. Grimmet. Birdlife International, Cambridge, 1994.

The Birds of the Western Palearctic. Concise edition. Volume 1. Edited by D.W. Snow and C.M. Perrins. Oxford University Press, 1998.

The EBCC Atlas of European Breeding Birds, their Distribution and Abundance. Edited by W.J.M. Hagemeijer and M. J Blair. T & A D Poyser, London, 1997.

Farms, Crofts and Corncrakes. A Guide to Habitat Management for Corncrakes. Leaflet on corncrake-friendly farming produced by the Steering Group for the Corncrake Biodiversity Action Plan. Copies available from offices of SNH, The Royal Society for the Protection of Birds, or The Scottish Executive Rural Affairs Department (SERAD).

Handbook of the Birds of the World. Volume 3. Edited by J. del Hoyo, A. Elliott and J. Sargatal. Published by Linx Edicions, Barcelona, 1992.

Management Scheme for Corncrakes in Special Protection Areas. Leaflet with information on a network of protected areas for corncrake and payments available to support 'corncrake-friendly' management within these Special Protection Areas. Copies available from SNH.

The New Atlas of Breeding Birds in Britain and Ireland: 1988-1991, compiled by David Wingfield Gibbons, James B Reid and Robert A Chapman. Published by T & A D Poyser, 1993.

Operation Survival. A Celebration of People and Nature in Scotland, by S-A Wilson. Book accompanying a BBC Scotland series which includes a chapter about corncrakes on the island of Coll. Mainstream Publishing Company (Edinburgh), 1996.

The Decline of the Corncrake in Britain Continues. By R. Green, 'Bird Study', 1995, volume 42, pages 66-75.

The status of the Corncrake Crex crex in Britain in 1998. By Rhys E. Green and David W. Gibbons 'Bird Study', 2000, volume 47, pages 129-137.

Vogelwelt 118 Parts 3-4 (1997). Special edition of ornithological journal devoted to corncrakes, including papers in English and German.

In addition, a world bibliography of corncrakes is being compiled on the internet and can be found at: www.lbv.de/Crex/bibliographie_e.htm

Useful addresses

Scottish Natural Heritage
2-5 Anderson Place
Edinburgh EH6 5NP

The Scottish Executive Rural Affairs Department
Environment Group
Victoria Quay
Edinburgh EH6 6QQ

The Royal Society for the Protection of Birds
Dunedin House
25 Ravelston Terrace
Edinburgh EH4 3TP

Also in the Naturally Scottish series...

If you have enjoyed Lichens why not find out more about Scotland's wildlife in our Naturally Scottish series. Each booklet looks at one or more of Scotland's native species. The clear and informative text is illustrated with exceptional photographs by top wildlife photographers, showing the species in their native habitats and illustrating their relationships with man. They also provide information on conservation and the law.

Amphibians and Reptiles

Although there are only six amphibians and three reptiles native to Scotland, these delightful animals have been part of our culture for a long time. They feature on Pictish stones and in a play - 'The Puddock and the Princess'.
ISBN 1 85397 401 3 pbk 40pp £4.95

Badgers

With its distinctive black and white striped face and short, squat body, the badger is probably one of the most popular mammals in Britain. Packed with stunning photographs, this publication reveals some amazing facts about the shy, secretive badger.
Mairi Cooper & John Ralston
ISBN 1 85397 254 1 pbk 16pp £3.00

Bumblebees

Did you know that Bummiebee, Droner and Foggie-toddler are all Scottish names for the bumblebee? Find out what these names mean and why bumblebees are so special inside this beautifully illustrated booklet. Also discover how you can help the bumblebee by planting appropriate flowers for their continued survival.
Murdo Macdonald
ISBN 1 85397 364 5 pbk 40pp £4.95

Burnet Moths

Unlike many other species of moth, burnet moths fly by day. They can be easily recognised by their beautiful, glossy black wings with crimson spots. Their striking colouring is a very real warning to predators.
Mark Young
ISBN 1 85397 209 6 pbk 24pp £3.00

Fungi

Fungi belong to one of the most varied, useful and ancient kingdoms in the natural world. Scotland may have almost 2000 larger species with some of the most interesting found in our woodlands and grasslands. This booklet provides an introduction to their life cycles, habitats and conservation. Discover the fascinating forms of earthstars, truffles and waxcaps.
Roy Watling MBE and Stephen Ward
ISBN 1 85397 341 6 pbk 40pp £4.95

Lichens

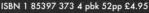

There are more than 1700 species of lichen occurring throughout the British Isles, and many grow in Scotland where the air is purer. Several different species may be found on a single rock or tree, resulting in lichenologists spending hours in one spot!
Oliver Gilbert
ISBN 1 85397 373 4 pbk 52pp £4.95

Red Kites

This graceful and distinctive bird was absent from Scotland's skies for more than a century. Now with the help of a successful programme of re-introduction, it's russet plumage and forked tail can once again be seen in Scotland.
David Minns and Doug Gilbert
ISBN 1 85397 210 X pbk 24pp £3.95

Red Squirrels

The red squirrel is one Scotland's most endearing mammals. This booklet provides an insight into their ecology and some of the problems facing red squirrels in Scotland today.
Peter Lurz & Mairi Cooper
ISBN 1 85397 298 4 pbk 20pp £3.00

River Runners

Scotland's clean, cascading rivers contain a fascinating array of species. The atlantic salmon is the best known of our riverine species but others, such as lampreys and freshwater pearl mussels, are frequently overlooked but no less captivating. This booklet aims to illuminate aspects of their intriguing and largely unseen lifecycles, habitats and conservation measures.
Iain Sime
ISBN 1 85397 353 X pbk 44pp £4.95

Sea Eagles

This magnificent bird, with its wing span of over 2m is the largest bird of prey in Britain. In 1916 they became extinct, but a reintroduction programme began in 1975. This booklet documents the return of this truly majestic eagle. Production subsidised by Anheuser-Busch.
Greg Mudge, Kevin Duffy, Kate Thompson & John Love

SNH Publications Order Form:
Naturally Scottish Series

Title	Price	Quantity
Amphibians & Reptiles	£4.95	
Badgers	£3.00	
Bumblebees	£4.95	
Burnet Moths	£3.00	
Corncrakes	£3.95	
Fungi	£4.95	
Lichens	£4.95	
Red Kites	£3.95	
Red Squirrels	£3.00	
River Runners	£4.95	
Sea Eagles	£1.50	

Postage and packing: free of charge in the UK, a standard charge of £2.95 will be applied to all orders from the European Union. Elsewhere a standard charge of £5.50 will be applied for postage.

Please complete in BLOCK CAPITALS

Name _____

Address _____

_____

_____

_____ Post Code

Type of Credit Card   VISA ☐   MasterCard ☐

Name of card holder _____

Card Number

☐☐☐☐ ☐☐☐☐ ☐☐☐☐ ☐☐☐☐

Expiry Date ☐☐ ☐☐

Send order and cheque made payable to Scottish Natural Heritage to:

Scottish Natural Heritage. Design and Publications, Battleby, Redgorton, Perth PH1 3EW

pubs@snh.gov.uk
www.snh.org.uk

Please add my name to the mailing list for the: SNH Magazine ☐

Publications Catalogue ☐